# Chapter Nine
## More Literary Dev

A variety of **Literary Devices** can make your writing more interesting and colourful. They can help you improve your use of language and communicate your ideas more effectively. We will explore the use of the following Literary Devices:

- **Imagery, Simile and Metaphor**
- **Exaggeration, Caricature and Emotive Language**
- **Symbols and Talismans**
- **Assonance, Alliteration and Onomatopoeia**

## 1. Imagery, Simile and Metaphor

The use of **Imagery** in language evokes sensory experience. Some kinds of language create 'pictures in the mind' where combinations of the five senses (seeing, smelling, tasting, hearing, touching) are activated. This can also be achieved with Descriptive Language as we have already explored (Book 1).

Two Literary Devices are especially useful for this:

A **Simile** is where the words *'like'* or *'as'* are used to compare two different ideas.

Examples:
'*He flew <u>like an eagle</u>*' or '*She was <u>as brave as a lion</u>*'.

A **Metaphor** is similar to a simile but the comparison is more direct since *'like'* and *'as'* are not used.

Examples:
'*Her hair <u>stood on end</u>*' or '*In the first drama lesson the teacher played a getting-to-know-you game to <u>break the ice</u>*'.

Similes and Metaphors are 'heightened language' as they convey ideas and images quickly. This is particularly useful in poetry.

**Make use of Imagery in *'The Crash'* story by employing Metaphors and Similes.**

Metaphors are indicated with bold type only.

Similes are shown with bold type and underlining.

A reminder of the story so far. John is faced with a crucial decision: does he pursue Noakes or not? Now we find out.

'*John watched Noakes ease himself back into the vehicle. The **engine growled** and burst into life. It revved up and moved off. Eddy jumped up and stood **full square** in the middle of the road. He held up his arm for Noakes to stop but John knew he would not. Eddy's huge frame was no match for a sports car. He was tossed over the bonnet **<u>like a rag doll</u>**.*

*John watched the car roar away, just as the ambulance screeched to a halt. Suddenly, there were paramedics pushing past him. Eddy was moaning in agony but John knew he was in the best of hands. John's legs **<u>felt like jelly</u>** but he shook with rage. For a moment John hesitated, then he knew what he had to do...*

*John rushed to the police car and climbed in. He could still see the distant lights of Noakes' car. John took a deep breath and hit the accelerator. As he sped along the narrow road he saw Noakes take the exit onto the dual carriageway. John knew Noakes was gaining on him. Noakes almost lost control as the back wheels of the car slid round. The rear bumper glanced off the barrier and **exhaust choked** from the back as Noakes struggled to regain control. John zipped onto the inside lane and his **car screamed** into high revs. He looked across into Noakes' car. For a brief moment Noakes turned his head and their eyes locked. Noakes' threat about stealing a sports car flashed back into John's mind.*

*It seemed like time stood still. Everything seemed to go into slow motion. There he was in the bright red Porsche. Proud and*

# 11+
# English
# Creative Writing

## WORKBOOK 5

**Stephen C. Curran**

Edited by Andrea Richardson and Warren Vokes

Sub-editor: Katrina MacKay

This book belongs to

TUITION

Accelerated Education Publications Ltd.

# Contents

*arrogant behind the wheel **like a strutting peacock**. Suddenly his eyes flashed with hatred and loathing and he flung the wheel to the left. The sleek **panther-like body** of the Porsche accelerated across John's path. His heart nearly came up into his mouth as he hit the brakes. A cloud of dust and smoke belched up from the road as the wheels of the Porsche screamed on the tarmac. John desperately tried to regain control. Through the haze he could just make out the crimson tail lights in the distance. John's hands were shaking and his terror was palpable but his anger was stronger.*

*John rammed down the accelerator and was right behind Noakes. The Porsche suddenly slunk off left up a track. John saw the 'No Entry' sign. The Porsche smashed right through it and onto the quarry road. It was pitch black. The cars bounced and skidded across the shingle as they climbed the hill. The road turned sharply and the Porsche almost went over the edge into the valley below. John was right behind him **like a cheetah after its quarry**. He skilfully steered into the skid just in time. The road suddenly narrowed and then there was no road.'*

**Exercise 9: 1** Place the Similes and Metaphors in appropriate positions in this story, *'A Day on the Ice'*.

Similes

| | |
|---|---|
| *like excitable husky dogs* | *like water down an open plug hole* |
| *as hard as steel*    *like a sheet of glass* | *a whip-like crack* |

Metaphors

| | | |
|---|---|---|
| *blanket of snow* | *clawed at his muscles* | *flowing white silk* |
| *desperate howls of the local farmer* | *feathery snow-covered ice* | |

*'Graham and his younger brother Miles loved the snow. They had been looking forward to the first snowfall for weeks. On the day a ................................ fell they went out to play near a local lake.*

*It looked just ........................................................ with a thin sheen of velvety snow covering the surface. Graham wanted to venture out onto the frozen lake so he could slide on the ice. They dragged their sledge ........ ........................................ onto the ice. They did not hear the ........................................................ to get off the ice because it was dangerous. He had spotted them a few minutes earlier as he was on his way to a nearby field. To the boys, it looked thick enough to hold their weight. When they walked on the ice it seemed as if it was ........................................ . It was not long before they were running about and sliding their sledge on the ................................................ .*

*Suddenly Miles heard ................................................ . A gaping hole opened up and his foot slipped down below the surface into the icy waters. Then more ice caved in and, before he knew it, he found himself falling through the ice into the frozen lake. Graham was soon there, reaching out a hand, but Miles felt he was being sucked beneath the surface of the ice ................................................ . Then more ice gave way and he was up to his waist in freezing water. He thrashed about as paralysing icy water ................................................ .*

*Fortunately, the farmer heard the screams of the boys, rushed to the lake shore and used a rope to pull them free. The boys had learned their lesson about playing on the ice. The ................................................ . had looked so inviting but it held hidden dangers.'*

# 2. Exaggeration, Caricature and Emotive Language

**Exaggeration**, **Caricature** and **Emotive Language** are literary devices that are used to distort the truth. They make things seem bigger or more important than they really are, through what characters say, or through Narrative Description.

Exaggeration - This is where the impression of something given in speech or writing makes it seem larger or more important than it really is.

e.g. *'I was so thirsty after sports day I could have drunk up all the water in the local swimming pool.'*

Caricature - This is where a person's characteristic traits are represented in a grotesque or comic way through a drawing or in description by using Similes and Metaphors.

e.g. *'The man had huge, bulbous eyes like a frog. He sat sprawling across his sofa as if it was a huge waterlily leaf lying on the surface of a pond.'*

Emotive Language - This is where extreme or exaggerated forms of language in Narrative or Speech are characterised by high levels of emotion. In other words, rational thinking is often set aside and emotions control what is said.

e.g. *'All people who eat meat are cruel, vicious and have no concern for animals or conservation.'*

Example: 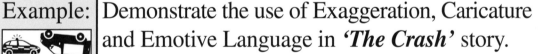 Demonstrate the use of Exaggeration, Caricature and Emotive Language in *'The Crash'* story.

*'And then it happened: it was like a vision - a moment of realisation; after all these years, John had remembered the crash...*

*A car barrels towards them; a green sedan - completely out of control. Mum and Dad are in the front. Dad is laughing at some joke. Dad is always telling jokes but we never find them funny - that is the joke. He is so bad at it. Only I had seen it; a distant speck heading towards us; closer and closer; the sudden impact;*

*the crumbling, twisting of steel; the tangled wreckage, jagged shards of glass rake the compartment.* **Everybody is flung mercilessly forward into the torn, pointed metal, like puppets across a stage. Then the silence, the pungent smell of burning oil and plastic. As flames engulf the car I lie on top of the blood-stained and lifeless forms of my mum and dad...**

**1**

*John realised he was still driving; and driving very fast. It almost seemed as if he had blacked out. Somehow instinct had taken over. He had remembered everything from those terrible moments. But here he was; Noakes was still out in front but John was closing on him. He was no longer shaking. All his anger about his past was now directed towards Noakes.*

*John found himself shouting,* **"You spotted, puny teenager. I'll teach you! Scrawny little Bart Simpson look-a-like."**

**2**

*After this angry outburst John was strangely calm. This new confrontation with Noakes, and remembering the details of the crash all those years ago, had somehow purged him. He was still afraid but he knew he had come back from death once before. More details flooded back into his mind. In some way their bodies had broken the impact. His parents had saved his life. The past came into sharp relief...*

*Moments after the crash; John thinks again. I am alive, still breathing, but trapped. I hear sirens. My eyes focus; the pain wracks my body. In front, the smashed-up green sedan lies still. Then a movement; the door cranks open. A young man clambers out, staggers across the road towards me and looks in. His face is bruised and his eyes bulge. He lifts a bottle of whisky to his lips and slakes his thirst. Then he drains the bottle of every last drop and tosses it aside. He burps loudly, then walks off*

8                                                    © 2009  Stephen Curran  ae

*unsteadily into the night...*

*John now remembered the face of the man. He had always known a drunk driver had killed his parents but he could never remember the man's face. Now he did; the features were etched in his mind.* **His eyes had rolled with amusement; his fixed uncaring gaze, 3 vicious and inhuman, like a ferocious lion about to devour his prey.** *John also recalled the man had turned round one last time and slurred some words under his breath before he staggered away.* **4 "Stupid Sunday drivers, don't know how to drive, do you?"**

*John knew he had to stop Noakes; that same cold, vicious look was in his eyes. John was now right behind Noakes. Then Noakes suddenly swerved left up a track. John saw the 'danger' sign. The Porsche crashed right through it and towards the old quarry road: the most dangerous place in the district. The tail lights of the Porsche were out in front, swinging from right to left. The pits and troughs of the rough-hewn track punished the suspension of the squad car.* **Its frail metal frame bounced and landed precariously like an out-of-control speedboat on a choppy sea. 5**

*John rammed down the accelerator until his foot hit the floor. The track steepened and suddenly the Porsche pulled sharply to the right. There was a screech of brakes and the stench of burning rubber. John realised too late that it was a trap. The Porsche cleared the wall of piled-up stones by a whisker but John had not seen the obstacle in time. The car plunged forward as in slow-motion towards the wall of boulders. The seconds seemed to lengthen as John stood on the brakes and the car careered towards the wall. He flung the steering wheel desperately to the left and the car went into a controlled skid but it would never be enough to clear the wall.*

*Then came a loud thud and a grinding sound as metal met immovable rock. The front glanced against the wall, failing to trigger the air bag and John was propelled forward; his chest rammed against the steering wheel. He gasped as the air was forced out of his lungs and his head hit the dashboard. The back end of the car swung round and slammed against the wall of rock, sending a thumping after-shock through the flimsy metal frame that shattered every window in the car. A warm stream of blood pumped from a large gash in John's forehead. He was in a daze and the insides of the car seemed like they were spinning.*

*There was a voice echoing in the distance. Then it came into focus. Noakes was standing by the side of the battered police car.*

**6** ***"You stupid weakling; you can't catch me. You're pathetic."*** *Noakes was screaming abuse. John was delirious and could hardly make out his rants.*

***Noakes drew in close, "You know what you look like - a smashed-up crash dummy. Yeah, like a stuffed dummy."*** **7**

*John coughed and felt the warm blood in his mouth. He spat it out and sank back on the seat in agony. The steering wheel had cut deep into his chest and he knew some ribs were broken. Then he heard raucous laughter; Noakes was actually laughing at him.*

***John summoned all his strength, "You little monster!" He gasped for air, "I'll get you, you're a killer, a murderer!"*** **8**

*John heard the sound of distant footsteps and a car door creak and slam. He cranked his head painfully to the left and glimpsed the glowing red brake lights of the Porsche some fifty yards away.*

 æ

*As his eyes smarted from the perspiration, the lights seemed to blur into gigantic whirlpools of steaming hot blood. He blinked and the swirling red mass appeared to cascade towards him.* **9**

*There was a growl and the Porsche revved up; wheels spun furiously and in a second it was away into the darkness. John knew he could be badly hurt and the car was a mess. He could still move his feet although his hands were shaking with the shock. His breaths were shallow and he felt like vomitting.*

*For a few seconds he sat and felt the despair wash over him. It was over; he had lost and Noakes had won. He would always lose and things would never go right for him.*

*The tears streamed down his cheeks and mingled with the blood as he muttered to himself, "I'm sorry Dad, I let you down. I'm useless; a failure."*

## Exercise 9: 2

Examine the nine highlighted passages in *'The Crash'* story. Write whether they are Exaggeration, Emotive Language or Caricature. There are three of each type.

Write Exaggeration, Emotive Language or Caricature in the spaces below:

**1.** ................................................

**2.** ................................................

**3.** ................................................

**4.** ................................................

**5.** ................................................

**6.** ................................................

**7.** ................................................

**8.** ................................................

**9.** ................................................

# 3. Symbols and Talismans

A **Symbol** is an image or an object that represents or recalls an idea or quality. In other words, it is visual or written short-hand that conveys something immediately to the onlooker or reader. It can be used repeatedly in a story to re-introduce an idea or theme back into the story.

Examples of Symbols include the following:
• Colours are often used. White dresses stand for purity in a wedding. Red lights stand for danger and green for safe on the road. Purple stands for royalty and is often worn by the monarch. Green can also stand for spring or youthfulness.
• A religious object, like a cross, represents Christianity. This image is often used to indicate the power of goodness in vampire stories. The wands of witches or wizards, pointed hats and books of spells indicate magical power.
• An item of jewellery or a keepsake can stand for a loved one.
• Elements like fiery flames can represent great power and flowing water can stand for new life and wholeness.
• Pictures or images can represent ideas. For instance, road signs contain images - a circle for a roundabout, a cross for crossroads or a curved line for a sharp bend.

Example: | Show how a Symbol can be used effectively to carry a Theme in *'The Tunnel'* story.

We rejoin Benjy as he tries to avoid recapture. In the process, he makes an important discovery that has symbolic significance.

*'Footsteps, then torchlight flashed across the roof of the cavern as Hoppity emerged. He was breathing heavily with concern.*

*"Come on Dave, we've lost him. Let's get out before the police arrive."*

*Dave was silent for a moment.*

*"You think I'm gonna give this up? Listen, this is my big chance. I've had nothing all my life. That brat will pay for what he's done to my son."*

*"This isn't about the boy is it? It's about you."*
*Dave charged across the cavern, collared Hoppity and rammed him up against wall.*

*"No one looks down on me, do you hear? No one!" Dave's grip tightened and Hoppity began to suffocate.*

*He choked, "Alright, okay!"*
*Dave released him suddenly. Hoppity fell back gasping for air.*

*Dave rasped, "He must have taken one of the other passages."*

*"What if he's fallen down the old mine shaft?"*
*Dave's lips tightened. He brushed away the sweat from his brow.*

*"Won't be just kidnapping then."*

*Dave raised his fist, "Shut up! Come on."*
*Moments later they had both disappeared into the blackness.'*

**The Symbol of the Drawings is introduced into the story. A connection with ancient peoples and human sacrifice is suggested.**

*'A mine shaft? I struggled to think. There are no mines in Radley; well none that I knew of. Then I recalled - Dumpy's adventure. He kept talking about his big discovery - some old river bed leading to an opening in a hill. Then he claimed he nearly fell over the edge; must have been the head of the shaft. We all laughed at him as usual. He was trying to impress us. What a joke! I never believed a word of it. Dumpy said he had climbed down into the shaft and had found some old caves. **He talked about exploring the caves and then finding something strange; some amazing drawings on***

*the wall. He thought he had discovered the old caves our history teacher talked about. Local archaeologists had been searching for them for decades, after some miners once said they had found them many years ago. Legends claimed ancient peoples had sacrificed to their gods in the caves. We thought Dumpy was seeing things; just telling tales.* We laughed till we cried. Dumpy was so fat we thought he probably rolled down into the shaft.

As I carefully edged my way along the wall, I noticed something glowing on the floor; a mobile phone. I shuffled towards it; my foot slipped, kicked the mobile and it clattered downwards. The echo reverberated about the cavern. I felt my leg dangling in mid-air and nearly fell over the edge. I balanced precariously on the precipice. I had found Dumpy's mine shaft. Phew! That was close. I laid face down and peered over the edge. The shining blue face of the mobile lit up the ledge it was resting upon. On the other side of the shaft, just below the ledge, I could see a large hole. It looked like the mouth of a cavern. The dull, blue light of the mobile reflected off the sides of the opening.'

**These ancient drawings show a group of angry hunters surrounding a terrified young boy.**

*'Then I saw it - a drawing in white carved over the top of the opening. I strained my eyes to make out the details. It looked like a group of hunters waving spears and weapons. There was an animal in the middle. No, it wasn't an animal. It looked like a man, a small man or maybe a boy. It was a boy; it must be because he was so much smaller than all the hunters. Their faces were full of anger and his; of terror. Primitive, yes, but the emotions were clear. This was Dumpy's discovery. Dumpy*

*had obviously found it from the opening in the hill. The shaft was about fifteen feet across. I knew there was a huge drop. Both sides of the shaft almost touched the walls of the tunnel. It looked like there was a very narrow ledge round the edge of the shaft, but it was incredibly dangerous to cross. Now I knew I could escape; there was a way out but how would I get across to the other side?*

*Then I heard noises again. Voices echoed in the tunnel behind me. It was Dave and his accomplice, Hoppity, no doubt on their way. Light flickered on the side of the cave walls. I knew I had no choice, so I took off my shoes for better grip. I clambered along the side of the shaft, ramming my back up against the tunnel wall. The descending narrow ledge was barely six inches wide. My feet and ankles strained to keep me upright and I swayed unsteadily. The tiny walkway was slippery and part of it seemed to crumble as my feet touched it. Loose stones slipped off the ledge into the darkness. There was a long silence and then a tiny thud as they hit the bottom. It was a long way down and I knew it would be certain death if I fell. My pulse quickened and I felt beads of clammy sweat under my collar, even though the tunnel was cold and damp.*

*Suddenly the voices were distinct. I froze with terror.*

*"I tell you, he must have come up this way. He could never have got past us."*

*Hoppity chipped in, "Look Dave, let's leave it, we can stop this now, pretend it was all a joke gone wrong."*

*Dave screamed, "You just don't get it do you? I'm going to get the money; then I'll go away. Live the life I was supposed to. I've never had anything. That's all changing. He's on his way, Benjy's big 'fat-cat' daddy. He'll be outside the entrance in twenty minutes."*

"How? You lost your phone two hours ago."

Dave thundered, "I phoned him before that you idiot."

"You're crazy. How you gonna give the boy over for the money? There is no boy, he's gone. And the police; maybe he called them?"

Dave's voice became shrill, "He won't, you cretin, because I said I'd kill the boy."

Hoppity whined, "I just want out. I'm leaving right now."

"No you don't, you moron!"

I heard a scream, a heavy thud, loud groans, then silence.

"Hey Hoppity, wake up, I didn't mean it. Damn, what d'you keep goading me for? I didn't wanna do for you too."

Then I heard a loud dragging sound. I sidled along the ledge in desperation. With one final leap, I made it to the other side. My foot slipped off the edge but I managed to find a handhold as I tipped backwards. I hauled myself up and sat exhausted for a few moments on the other side. Dave's back suddenly came into view, as he pulled something near to the edge of the shaft. I looked down to where the mobile lay. The fall must have affected the electronics, as the blue light still glowed and Dave would certainly see it. I had to reach it. I slid my legs over the edge of the shaft and eased myself further down to the ledge, just as Dave peered over the mouth of the shaft. I snatched up the mobile and crouched inside the mouth of the small cave, under the ledge. I heard Dave heaving and blowing and more dragging sounds from up above. Dave's shadow flitted across the roof of the tunnel as he laid his flashlight down.

Suddenly something crashed past me. It hit the sides of the shaft as it tumbled down. For a split second I caught sight of ruffled and torn clothing. It was Hoppity. He had killed Hoppity. A few *moments later there was a splash, as the body hit the bottom of the shaft hundreds of feet below. Seconds passed; torch-light beams searched out the crevices in the shaft. I pulled myself back into the cave as the penetrating white beam exposed the crevices and cracks in the rock around me. For a second I held my breath. I knew he was listening for the slightest sound or movement. I clutched the mobile tightly to obscure the dull, blue light.*

*There were scuffles as he drew back from the edge.*

 *Then he roared in a high-pitched scream, "Benjy I know you can hear me. If I miss this appointment and I don't get the money I'll find you and I'll kill you."*
*The words reverberated repeatedly off the walls of the cavern and through the tunnel system. I heard the echo of footsteps down the tunnel and in a flash he was gone, but for how long?*

*Maybe I should give myself up. Perhaps he would just exchange me for the money and that would be it. But he had already murdered Hoppity; he was crazy. I'd probably end up at the bottom of the shaft too. My fingers uncurled and the mobile lay in my hand. I wondered if it worked. I pressed the menu to find the 'last call'. There it was; he had called my father. I hit the call button and pressed the mobile to my ear. Nothing! I pulled it away, the screen read 'no signal'. If I could only find a place where the mobile worked. The battery was running down because the light stayed on. I would have to be quick.'*

**The full implication of the drawings is understood. They show the brutality and cruelty of human sacrifice.**

'***Just as I was about to scramble out of the cave, I noticed there was more than one drawing on the wall. I held up the mobile and examined the other drawing to the right of the first. The*** *eerie, blue light flitted across the ancient stone carving and I could not make it out. As I carefully angled the face of the mobile towards it, a horrific image jumped into view. I gasped in horror. The hunters were captured, as in a photograph, in some dance. Their faces wore expressions of glee. In the centre was the mutilated corpse of the boy. As I pulled the mobile away from the gory scene, I could see there was one final carving beneath it. It showed the hunters throwing the body into an old well. It was a grim realisation; this was the place they disposed of the bodies; the old well had once been used by the miners as a shaft to the coal seam, until it became too dangerous. I suppose the miners had never realised the significance of the drawings - just some old grafitti they ignored.*

*I wondered if I would end up down there with all the old bones. A child forgotten; for thousands of years no one would ever know, until some damp, crusty skull was found by an archaeologist in the future.'*

**The drawings have a Symbolic link to the Story Theme. They show cruel and bullying treatment being meted out on a young boy by his tribe. Benjy treats his victims in an unfair and bullying manner just like the tribe. Hopefully Benjy will understand the connection and the implications of his bullying behaviour.**

A **Talisman** or Amulet is an image or an object which is supposedly endowed with protective or magical powers.

Examples might include:
An inscribed ring or Amulet, a charm or a special stone.
A Talisman is usually thought to bring good luck or to protect its wearer or the holder from evil or danger.

Show the use of a Talisman (an object with magic powers) in *'The Magic Key'* story.

Hannah is given a key for her thirteenth birthday. She is very disappointed. However, she does not realise it is a Talisman and has special powers.

*'Hannah had always enjoyed birthdays; well until this one. A few moments before, she had stood motionless, but very excited, before a large cake with exactly thirteen candles on it. She had slowly unwrapped the only gift in front of her with great anticipation. A knowing smile crept across her face as each layer peeled away, leaving at last a small box.*

*Hannah could not sleep the night before. She thought she had already worked out what Mum would buy her. There was the new dress she had pointed out in that designer shop last week. Mum had raised her eyes at the price but she did say she would think about it. Hannah thought it was as good as bought. Her best friend Josie always had the latest designer clothes, and Hannah imagined herself just for once being better dressed and more 'cool'. That would teach Josie!*

*Hannah would never forget that sinking feeling; a feeling you get when you try to look grateful, but you are not. It was just a key; a plain looking door key. She held it up and then looked inside the wrapping for something else. Her friend Josie looked smug in her new dress.*

*Astonishingly, Hannah's mum looked pleased with herself. She mumbled something about it opening something important but Hannah could only feel anger rising within her. After all, you do not become a teenager every day. What was wrong with her* mother? Could she not see this would be the biggest joke ever? Josie would never keep it a secret. The next day would be the first day back after the holidays, so the whole school would know by tomorrow. Hannah cried herself to sleep that night. As she slept **the key began to glow by her bedside**.'

**The key is a Talisman that has magical powers. It will open something special and bring good luck to Hannah.**

'Hannah woke up early as she always did. Her first thought, before the expectations and demands of the new day greeted her, was the bitter remembrance of her birthday party. What a disaster! Could things be any worse? She dragged herself out of bed, dreading what the day held.

**Hannah was now dressed and ready. As she made to leave, her eyes rested on the key on the bedside table. It seemed bigger than before. She picked it up and examined it. Hannah was sure it was just the size of an ordinary door key the day before. Now it was definitely bigger and heavier. In fact it seemed about twice the size and weight. It appeared to have a luminescent quality too. Very strange! Hannah felt somehow compelled to take it with her. She slipped it into her school bag and headed towards the door.**

As Hannah nibbled on a piece of toast, her mother hummed away merrily near the stove. The tune for 'happy birthday to you' was beginning to grate on Hannah's nerves by now.

"More toast?" she lilted in a sing-song tone.

Hannah had not even eaten the first piece. She had completely lost her appetite.

"No thanks, I don't feel hungry."

Mother turned towards Hannah smiling broadly.

"Now, my sweet, you must look after yourself. After all you're a growing girl with everything before you."

Hannah felt exasperated. Mother still could not see it. She had ruined her birthday, made a complete laughing-stock of her and now she was worrying about a piece of toast. Mother did not understand anything. Hannah felt so nervous about facing her friends, she would vomit if she ate anything. What made it even worse was the fact that the first day back had been declared a mufti day. They could all wear their own clothes and there would be no designer dress for Hannah to show off.

Hannah said a cool goodbye after her mother had planted on her an unwanted birthday kiss. She dawdled her way to St. Bridget's Girls' School. On arrival, Hannah quickly made her way to the lockers. Sure enough, there was Josie standing in a little huddle with some other girls from the class. They were whispering and giggling. Hannah had no doubt about what they were discussing.

Every now and then Josie shot a glance towards Hannah, then plunged back into excited conversation with her new found friends. Hannah felt very annoyed and she knew she was blushing. It would be difficult to hide her irritation, so she quickly placed her books, packed lunch and the key in her locker.'

**Hannah begins to realise for the first time there is something special about this key.**

'**Just before she closed the locker door she noticed the key again. It appeared to have a magnetic quality and she could not take her eyes off it. Hannah peered into the locker. She felt certain the key was glowing. The inside of the locker was bathed** *in yellow light. Was it her eyes? She blinked and stared. It was still there and she was not seeing things.*

"Hi, Miss Birthday Girl," Josie joked. The two sidekicks, Miriam and Paula, giggled.
Hannah panicked and slammed the locker door.
"Bit jumpy aren't we?" Josie goaded.
The giggles came again and Miriam stared up at Hannah. She was spotty and her hair was lank. Paula was prettier but her voice was high-pitched and rasping. So Josie had thrown her over for these two specimens who spent all their time gossiping and making up stories about others. Josie stood there in her new designer skirt and top. She always had new clothes and they were always stunning.

Hannah self-consciously hovered on the spot and wished the ground would swallow her up. She was dressed in that frumpy old number from last season. No one with any fashion sense would be seen dead in it. And yet, here was Hannah trying to face down three of the class's fashion icons. She felt stupid. The dress was too small, clung to her in all the wrong places and was the wrong colour. I ask you, who would wear bright green this year, she thought to herself. Hannah could see these three girls ogling and she knew they could read her thoughts.

"You look great Hannah," Paula drooled sarcastically. Miriam smirked and looked away to hide her laughter.
"Yeah Hannah, green's in I think. Isn't it, Miriam?" Miriam was pretending to cough but was really overcome with the giggles. Josie twirled in front of Hannah in her exquisite outfit.
"Do you like mine?" Josie jeered.
Hannah nodded unconvincingly. She felt hot and bothered. Other

classmates were passing by and Hannah knew they were all looking at her. Josie was enjoying Hannah's embarassment.

"By the way Hannah, it's my birthday party on Saturday. You will be there won't you? Dressed to kill I hope!"

Hannah tried to sound confident, "Of course."

One other class-member overheard the conversation and hovered nearby. It was Frances. For a few moments Hannah felt better as Frances was shabbily dressed, absolutely hopeless at sports, full of freckles and, worst of all, wore round, pebbled glasses.

"Can I come to the party Josie?" Frances pleaded. Josie's clan laughed until they almost cried. Hannah felt relieved as it took pressure off her. Frances stomped off in tears as usual.

Hannah knew the rest of the day would be horrific and the remainder of the term would not be much better. She now wished she had not told Josie how much she was looking forward to her birthday and about the new clothes she knew her mother had bought for her. It was too tempting. Hannah knew she would be popular if Josie liked her. Josie was the most-liked girl in the class, possibly in the school. But Josie was a fair-weather friend; she went with you if it suited her. Now it did not suit her. In fact, Josie had a way of being cruel. When Josie rejected people, she did not just ignore them. No, Hannah would now be the most unpopular girl in the class - relegated to obscurity and the object of scorn and humiliation.

After a dreadful day at school, running the gauntlet of the canteen, the cruel classroom banter and the long walk home alone, Hannah had had enough. She was desperate. As she approached her house, she passed the clothes shop. The dress was still right in the centre of the display. It was a deep red and almost shone under the spotlights. Hannah again imagined herself wearing that designer dress. She determined that somehow, in some way, she would have that dress. Hannah dreaded the thought of Josie's party. Only if she had the dress could she face down Josie and her cronies.'

## Exercise 9: 3

Decide whether the images or objects below are purely Symbols or also carry the magical power of a Talisman.

| ring | rabbit's foot | St. Christopher | dove | horseshoe |
|------|---------------|-----------------|------|-----------|
| coat of arms | garlic | crucifix | heart shape | poppy |

Remember:

A Symbol is an image or object that represents or stands for something else (i.e. an idea, a quality or a thing).

A Talisman is also a Symbol but it has an extra dimension. It is an object that supposedly has magical or protective powers.

Symbols:

1. ................................. stands for romantic love
2. ................................. a symbol of peace and gentleness
3. ................................. a sign of fidelity and commitment
4. ................................. remembrance of the dead in war
5. ................................. represents an important family

Talismans:

6. ................................. God's protection against evil forces
7. ................................. good luck or fortune
8. ................................. keeping away vampires at night
9. ................................. safety in travel and on long journeys
10. ................................ protection of the home from evil

**Try to use Symbols and Talismans in your next story draft.**

# 4. Assonance, Alliteration and Onomatopoeia

Literary devices, usually found in Poetry, can also be used sparingly in prose writing to give it a poetic quality. This must be done in a subtle way, so as not to be too obvious.

Three Literary Devices are of particular use in this respect:

**Assonance** occurs where words carry repeated vowel sounds in a passage. We commonly see this device used in poetry, particularly at the end of lines in rhyming couplets.

Examples:
'The play was about a brave man who saved the whales.'
'The Everest expedition was led by an eminent explorer.'

**Alliteration** occurs where words carry the same consonant sound repeatedly. It normally refers to the consonants at the beginning of the words.

Examples:
'The dam ran dry during the drought and created a desert.'
'The waves washed violently against the sea wall in winter.'

Assonance and Alliteration can be used in a sentence or passage to link words and ideas together.

**Onomatopoeia** occurs where a word represents the sound it actually makes. The sound suggested by the word itself is simulated or contained within the word. Onomatopoeic words can put rhythm into a sentence. They can also create a soundscape in people's minds (i.e. suggest the sound in the readers's imagination).

Examples:
'James whacked the ball with the cricket bat.'
'Sheba the cat meowed loudly when she was hungry.'

Example: Show the use of Assonance, Alliteration and Onomatopoeia in *'The Magic Key'* story.

Examples of Assonance, Alliteration and Onomatopoeia are indicated with bold type.

'Hannah knew she would again have to face her cheerful mother. As she quietly closed the front door and tried to creep up the stairs without being noticed, she heard the sing-song joyful voice.

"Is that you dear?"

Hannah ignored her mother and continued. Then the hallway doors swung wide. Her mother, hair newly permed and eyes sparkling, smiled warmly.

**Hannah's heart sank like a stone. She did not want to discuss the day. What would she say? Mother always wanted every detail. Not today, not now; she tried to edge away.** **1**

Hannah blurted, "I've got lots of homework."

"On the first day? Poor you."

Hannah felt like crying and letting out all the pain but she knew the person standing in front of her was responsible for it. Hannah was furious with her mother but did not want to let the 'monster' out. **She knew where that would lead. A wild outburst would probably make it worse anyway. With downcast and weary eyes, Hannah withdrew and wound her way up the stairs.** **2**

"Oh by the way, have you used the key yet?"

"The key?" Hannah mumbled.

"Yes, haven't you worked it out yet?"

Hannah was even more exasperated. What on earth was she talking about? Was she mad? What use was some old key?

"Keys open things dear. That's what they're for."

Just then, her little sister put her head round the door. Hannah could see the look in the child's eyes. This was all Hannah needed. A five year old who wanted to play.

"No, not now!" Hannah growled.

Rita's eyes filled with tears.

Mother grasped her hand and pulled Rita up into her arms.

"Hannah's Miss Grumpy at the moment. It's the homework." If only she knew, Hannah thought and then made her way up the remainder of the stairs as fast as she could go. She was exhausted and would sleep off the depression.

Hannah woke in a sweat. It was dark and she was behind schedule. She angrily reached for her school bag, looking for her homework. **As she shook it wildly, a pile of books scuffed the sides and tumbled out with a thud. The key hit the wooden floor with a loud ping.** **3** It was still glowing. Hannah turned out the light, picked up the key and examined it. She knew her mum always talked about having strange experiences. She claimed she had special powers; could see things, and objects moved when she did not expect them to. Hannah never believed a word of it; but the key, was she imagining it? Earlier she thought it was luminous but now it seemed to be shining.

Suddenly, she felt the key was dragging her towards the window. Its power was so strong it seemed like a dog pulling on a leash. Hannah went with it but soon found the pull of the key so intense it began to slip through her fingers. All at once she let the key go. **Hannah stared in stupefaction as it streaked towards the pane.** **4** **The key struck the glass with force like a deliberately flung stone.**

Hannah looked out across the empty street below. The street light over the road lit the small parade of shops. Her eyes rested upon the clothes shop. It pained her to look at it. The designer dress she had loved was still in the showroom window. Hannah had deliberately gone the long way round on her way to school, so as to avoid seeing it. She was too tired on the way back. Hannah realised the key was still pressed hard against the window pane.

**Suddenly the window cracked; there was a huge bang and an almighty crash as glass tinkled and clattered all over the floor.** **5** Hannah jumped back. There was silence and then a tinkle as the key landed outside on the pavement below. Hannah crept out of her room and down the stairs. In a jiffy she was in the street. Hannah picked up the key and again it almost dragged her towards the shop like a homing pigeon looking for its loft.

In seconds, she found herself looking at the beautiful, sleek designer garment that, for three months, she had dreamt of owning. Now she knew she had to have that dress and the key seemed to know it too. Before she could even think it, the key had rammed itself in the lock and she was inside. In desperation she slid the dress off the mannequin. The £250 price tag dropped onto the floor.

**For a few seconds it seemed insane and her resolve began to wane; but then she realised all the pain had now drained away.** **6** Hannah knew it was stealing but somehow she did not feel responsible. Her conscience was clear and there was no guilt. **The magic key wanted her to have it; that was all that mattered.** **7** It made everything okay, even though she knew it was not honest. Hannah wrapped up the dress, slipped out the door, and locked it securely with the key. She dashed across the road to her own house. **Every careful step on the stairs seemed to creak and squeal.** **8**

*With the dress carefully stashed under the bed, Hannah crept between the sheets. She knew she would sleep soundly that night. She comforted herself with the thought that no one would ever know how she had obtained it. After all, she had not really stolen the dress because the key - she now knew it to be a 'magic key' - had led her to take it; in fact it almost seemed to want her to do it. She could only think that if her mother had some special powers, they had in some way passed to her.*

*Hannah was feeling content. Now all she had to think about was the party on Saturday. Just one more day and then the weekend.* **Hannah was desirous of seeing Josie's jaw drop, in that delicious moment when she would flounce in wearing a delectable dress.** **9** *That would shut them all up. Of course Hannah had not even considered the fact the dress was now missing from the display window. Within seconds Hannah drifted into contented sleep.'*

## Exercise 9: 4

Study the highlighted passages from **'The Magic Key'** story. Decide whether they are Alliteration, Assonance or Onomatopoeia. There are three of each type.

Write Alliteration, Assonance or Onomatopoeia against each number in the spaces below:

**1.** ........................................   **2.** ........................................

**3.** ........................................   **4.** ........................................

**5.** ........................................   **6.** ........................................

**7.** ........................................   **8.** ........................................

**9.** ........................................

# Your Own Story - Draft One

This is your chance to write your own story using one of the following scenarios as a starting point.

On the next page are two story scenarios. Choose either:

**Story 9 - *'Stranded'*** or

**Story 10 - *'Aliens'***

• Use the learning points in this chapter to help you write.

• Write Story 9 in this book. Once you have learnt the principles, you can write Story 10 on separate sheets of paper.

## More Literary Devices

Try and include ideas and techniques from this chapter.

### 1. Imagery, Simile and Metaphor

Imagery inspires the five senses. Similes use *'like'* or *'as'* to compare ideas (e.g. *'As strong as an ox'*). Metaphors are a more direct comparison (e.g. *'The car engine growled into life'*).

### 2. Exaggeration, Caricature and Emotive Language

These devices use distortion to make an idea seem more significant. Speech or Narrative can be Exaggerated (e.g. *'I was so hungry I could eat a horse'*). Caricature represents people in grotesque or comic ways (e.g. *'The boy had screwed up features like a hamster'*). Emotive Language is extreme and Emotionally charged (e.g. *'Cyclists are a nuisance and cause car accidents'*).

### 3. Symbols and Talismans

Symbols are images or objects that represent something (e.g. *flashing blue lights mean an emergency*). A Talisman is symbolic but is thought to have special powers (e.g. *a lucky charm*).

### 4. Assonance, Alliteration and Onomatopoeia

Assonance is repeated vowel sounds (e.g. *'R<u>ai</u>n fell on the pl<u>ai</u>n'*). Alliteration is repeated consonant sounds (e.g. *'<u>D</u>ig out the <u>d</u>itch and <u>d</u>rain it of <u>d</u>irty water'*). Onomatopoeia is where a word makes the sound it represents (e.g. *'The bell <u>clanged loudly</u>'*).

# First Draft - Story 9

## 'Stranded'
## Opening Scenario in Present Tense:

'*I drag myself up onto the beach exhausted. The sea heaves as the storm rages on in the darkness. After choking and belching, I finally cough up the sea-water from my lungs. For a moment I lie still; grateful to be alive. Eventually, I lift my soaked and weary head and look out across the lagoon. Just beyond it, the boat is breaking up on the rocks. It splinters, disintegrates and slips beneath the waves. I turn and face the shoreline. A long, sandy beach stretches out before me. As I peer into the gloom, I can make out the dim outline of palm trees and the silhouette of a mountain behind them. Where am I? I am stranded and lost. Will I ever escape?*'

# First Draft - Story 10

## 'Aliens'
## Opening Scenario in Past Tense:

'*No one believed me. They all laughed when I said the aliens had landed. I finally persuaded my friend, Lesley, to come with me to the clearing in the woods. By now, it was getting dark.*

*Lesley sneered, "What are they like, little green men with horns?" We trudged on silently up to the ridge above the trees. As we neared the clearing, we saw a faint glow. Suddenly, we fell back terrified as bright lights came towards us. The woodland lit up and the distant drone became a deafening noise. We crouched behind some bushes and shielded our eyes. The blinding glare faded. There was silence.*

*I whispered to Lesley, "Now do you believe me?"*'

---

Continue with either **Story 9** or **Story 10**, then use the Planning page to write down some more ideas for your story.

# Planning - 1st Draft
# Story 9 - 'Stranded'

*Now let's write a story.*

....................................................................................................................................

....................................................................................................................................

....................................................................................................................................

....................................................................................................................................

....................................................................................................................................

....................................................................................................................................

....................................................................................................................................

....................................................................................................................................

....................................................................................................................................

....................................................................................................................................

....................................................................................................................................

....................................................................................................................................

....................................................................................................................................

....................................................................................................................................

....................................................................................................................................

....................................................................................................................................

....................................................................................................................................

If you have chosen **Story 9** - **'Stranded'**, copy out the opening scenario on Story Page 1 - 1st Draft, then continue your story on the pages that follow.

# Planning - 1st Draft
# Story 10 - *'Aliens'*

*It's time for your own story.*

.................................................................................
.................................................................................
.................................................................................
.................................................................................
.................................................................................
.................................................................................
.................................................................................
.................................................................................
.................................................................................
.................................................................................
.................................................................................
.................................................................................
.................................................................................
.................................................................................
.................................................................................
.................................................................................
.................................................................................
.................................................................................
.................................................................................
.................................................................................
.................................................................................
.................................................................................

If you have chosen **Story 10 - *'Aliens'***, copy out the opening scenario on Story Page 1 - 1st Draft, then continue your story on the pages that follow.

# Story Page 1 - 1st Draft
## *'Stranded'* or *'Aliens'*

# Story Page 2 - 1st Draft
## *'Stranded'* or *'Aliens'*

.............................................................................

.............................................................................

.............................................................................

.............................................................................

.............................................................................

.............................................................................

.............................................................................

.............................................................................

.............................................................................

.............................................................................

.............................................................................

.............................................................................

.............................................................................

.............................................................................

.............................................................................

.............................................................................

.............................................................................

# Story Page 3 - 1st Draft
## *'Stranded'* or *'Aliens'*

# Story Page 4 - 1st Draft
## *'Stranded'* or *'Aliens'*

...........................................................................................................................

...........................................................................................................................

...........................................................................................................................

...........................................................................................................................

...........................................................................................................................

...........................................................................................................................

...........................................................................................................................

...........................................................................................................................

...........................................................................................................................

...........................................................................................................................

...........................................................................................................................

...........................................................................................................................

...........................................................................................................................

...........................................................................................................................

...........................................................................................................................

...........................................................................................................................

...........................................................................................................................

...........................................................................................................................

...........................................................................................................................

...........................................................................................................................

...........................................................................................................................

# Story Page 5 - 1st Draft
## *'Stranded'* or *'Aliens'*

...........................................................................................

...........................................................................................

...........................................................................................

...........................................................................................

...........................................................................................

...........................................................................................

...........................................................................................

...........................................................................................

...........................................................................................

...........................................................................................

...........................................................................................

...........................................................................................

...........................................................................................

...........................................................................................

...........................................................................................

...........................................................................................

...........................................................................................

...........................................................................................

...........................................................................................

...........................................................................................

# Story Page 6 - 1st Draft
## *'Stranded'* or *'Aliens'*

..............................................................................................................

..............................................................................................................

..............................................................................................................

..............................................................................................................

..............................................................................................................

..............................................................................................................

..............................................................................................................

..............................................................................................................

..............................................................................................................

..............................................................................................................

..............................................................................................................

..............................................................................................................

..............................................................................................................

..............................................................................................................

..............................................................................................................

..............................................................................................................

..............................................................................................................

..............................................................................................................

..............................................................................................................

| **Scores Out of Ten** | Spelling & Grammar → | | Creativity → | |

# Chapter Ten
## *The Story Climax*

There are various types of **Story Climax** that can be used. It is very important to select the most appropriate kind of Story Climax for your own story. There are three broad types of Story Climax:

**Character Confrontation • A Big Event**
**A Threat to Life**

## *1. Character Confrontation*

A **Character Confrontation** brings the story to a head by causing the Hero Character and the Opponent Character to clash in a final Conflict. This could be a physical fight or battle which might result in death. However, it can also be a verbal conflict where the Hero Character's ideas or beliefs will usually prevail over those of the Opponent Character.

Example: Bring *'The Crash'* story to a head with a big Character Confrontation.

As we enter the final stages of the story, look out for the big confrontation between John, the Hero Character, and Noakes, the Opponent Character.

*'In his imagination John could now see his father's face. He looked for disapproval but somehow the countenance was kind and seemed to be longing for something. In his mind's eye, John saw his father's hands reach out towards him.*

*John snapped out of it and came back to his senses. By some miracle, the engine of the car was still running. He had survived the crash; hatred for Noakes and all he stood for began to flood every cell in his body. From somewhere, a new strength pulsated through him and the pain was numbed. He eased the car into gear and manoeuvred it away from the wall. John felt the pain stab through his chest as he reached up to the radio on his lapel. He flicked it on; nothing, it must have been damaged in the crash.*

*John knew Noakes would head over the most dangerous stretch of road to make his escape. It went across the old quarry route, over a rickety and disused bridge. As John rammed the car into second gear, he heard a crunch in the gearbox and saw plumes of smoke issue from the exhaust in his mirror. Would the car make it up the incline? He had to try. Only one headlight was working and John saw an ominous red sign come into view. 'No Through Road - Danger of Rockfall'. The barrier across the road was already smashed; no doubt the work of Noakes.*

*John swung the car right, onto the old quarry road. Dark, jagged rocks overhung the road on both sides. It seemed the boulders were perched and could fall at any moment. The road was steeper now and John rammed the gear lever into first. The engine screamed as if in pain and the tyres slipped on the loose gravel. Nothing grew here successfully. Gnarled old trees and sparse vegetation made it seem like he was entering another world. The temperature gauge was now touching red. Just then the road levelled and he pushed the car into second gear.*

*"Danger passed," he thought. Then a crash; John saw a huge boulder roll across the road just behind him. He felt sweat ooze from his brow and fall onto his blood-soaked collar. John slowed*

*as he heard more rumbles from up above. A shower of gravel hit the roof and John ducked instinctively, even though he knew it would be no use. Another boulder smashed down in front of him and bounced across the track. John swerved to miss it. There would be more now. John's eyes narrowed. He knew it was only speed and skill that would get him out of there. The back wheels spun and the car sprang into life. More rocks tumbled down and John dodged this way and that way to avoid the obstacles. A glance at the speedometer showed 50 then 60 miles per hour.*

*In seconds he was through the danger and the car descended down the valley towards the bridge. Now he felt in control. It was as if he were one with the car. He could see the distant and welcoming lights of the town but only darkness awaited him in the valley below. As he neared the bridge, he could hear the sound of the fast flowing river that had claimed the lives of so many unsuspecting swimmers. Then he noticed a dark shadow by the old bridge. It was a car. The lights were switched off. It was the Porsche. Noakes must have abandoned it; he thought. The bridge was too dangerous to cross. Had he walked across?'*

**The Story Climax begins here. It commences with a minor confrontation and builds to a massive confrontation between the characters, where one character will win over the other.**

*'John drew up alongside the Porsche. As he did so, the window rolled down and Noakes slowly turned his head towards John.*

*"Thought I had lost you. Now for the final test and you haven't got the guts."*

*John gasped, "Don't be stupid, you'll never do it. Give yourself up now."*

Noakes snarled, "Then you better catch me."
The lights of the Porsche came on and the engine exploded into life. Noakes took off towards the bridge at speed, skidded into a full-turn and jack-knifed the car. It spun round and round and came to halt right in front of the bridge as if in pole position for a race. This kid could drive, there was no doubt of that. John followed, then sped up to try and head Noakes off. Too late; Noakes saw his manoeuvre and took off at high speed towards the flimsy wooden structure. In a second, the Porsche was on the rotten old planks of the bridge. It swung dangerously under the weight of the car. A few chunks of wood came away and fell into the water, over a hundred feet below.

John watched for a second or two, then he knew he had to pursue. The bridge would only hold two cars if he kept his distance. His car edged over the planking. He heard it creak below him. Noakes increased his speed as he saw the final stretch. More planks were missing and the bridge banked to one side, as some of its supports had fallen away. John saw it coming. Noakes had underestimated the camber and the car veered to the right, went into a tail spin, hit the end of the bridge and rolled. Up-ended, it perched precariously on the edge of the bridge. Smoked billowed from the engine and a lick of flame curled up above the wheels.

The bridge was now swinging from side to side. John stopped the car and eased himself across his seat. As he scrambled out the door he felt giddy and sick. He staggered towards the burning wreck. As he approached, the battered door opened and a hand reached out. It was shaking. Then a head appeared as Noakes tried in vain to pull himself from the wreck. John looked down at the pitiful specimen.

*John assessed the situation quickly. He looked inside. He recoiled in horror. Noakes's leg was almost severed and his left arm severely mangled. A pool of blood gathered on the wood. John began to reel. It was all happening again.*

*For a moment time seemed to stand still and John felt the hatred, then it began to subside. Noakes's piercing gaze of desperation paralysed him.*

*        "Please," he mouthed.*
*Then, John saw a boy; just a boy, a lost kid like himself all those years ago. He saw the pain in Noakes's eyes and the longing for something.*

*        "Alright kid! Hold on, I've got you."*
*The flames now overwhelmed the sides of the car and the bridge was beginning to burn like matchwood.*

*John knew he had to be quick. There was no time for ceremony. He dragged Noakes from the car, cradled him in his arms and made for the end of the bridge. Noakes was unconscious now and breathing intermittently. John felt the bridge start to give way under him; struts collapsed and the burning wreck of the Porsche slid off into the river below. He heard the explosion behind him and a ball of fire leapt up towards the bridge.*

*Now all behind him was completely engulfed in flames. A few more yards. Just as John stepped off the wood onto the gravel he felt it give way. He almost fell backwards but managed to steady himself. He gently dropped to his knees and placed Noakes in front of him on the damp grass. John saw the distant blue lights of emergency vehicles heading up the valley from the town. They must have seen the explosion. He had made it but would Noakes survive? He had no idea. Had all his efforts been in vain?'*

**Exercise 10: 1**

Using the story *‘Stranded’* or *‘Aliens’*, rewrite the Big Climax so that it has a significant Character Confrontation.

..........................................................................................................

..........................................................................................................

..........................................................................................................

..........................................................................................................

..........................................................................................................

..........................................................................................................

..........................................................................................................

..........................................................................................................

..........................................................................................................

..........................................................................................................

..........................................................................................................

..........................................................................................................

..........................................................................................................

..........................................................................................................

..........................................................................................................

..........................................................................................................

..........................................................................................................

..........................................................................................................

_____

_____

_____

_____

_____

_____

_____

_____

_____

_____

_____

## 2. A Big Event

A **Big Event** can also bring a story to a close. This Event usually involves the Hero and Opponent Character but they are not always brought into direct confrontation. The Event could be a natural disaster or a personal tragedy.

Example: Using *'The Dark Forest'* story, show how a Big Event can bring the story to a Climax.

We rejoin this story as Paul Langdon tries to persuade his brother, Jake, to leave the hideout and return home with him.

*'"Jake, you must come home with me," I plead. "Things can be different. You're being used here."*

All of a sudden the old man appears from the shadows.

He speaks in a monotone, "Now I have two boys. You will help make the carvings too."

I get up to leave. He thrusts me back.

"Not so fast. This is your new home now."

Jake smiles, "See Paul, we can do things together now."

The old man glares at me, his eyes like pin-pricks in the gloom.

Then he gestures, "This way, boy."

He makes off towards the far end of the cavern. It narrows suddenly and I find myself in a long, winding tunnel. All of a sudden, it opens out into a large alcove.

The old man points to a corner, "It's for you."

There is a bed and chest of drawers. A small carpet but not threadbare like Jake's. It seems as if everything has been prepared for my arrival.

"You knew I would come?"

The old man draws closer, "Jake believed you would come one day. He's special. He has premonitions; visions of the future."

For the first few days of the confinement I wanted to escape. I suggested it to Jake on every possible occasion but he showed little interest. To my astonishment, I gradually realised Jake actually wanted to be there. He was not a prisoner and had no desire to leave. To be honest I could have run at any point. Nothing stopped me leaving except for one thing. I knew Jake would not come with me.

The daily routine was monotonous. We both slept in the hollow of the cavern on two roughly hewn beds. We rose at first light and took a simple breakfast, usually eaten in silence. It consisted *of food foraged from the forest and whatever the old man had managed to buy at the local market, about two miles away. Then we washed as best we could in the nearby stream. Soon we were collecting wood for the latest project. We looked for fallen trees on the forest floor, or cut branches from trees that had plenty of growth. On returning to the hideout, we would begin work.*

*As the winter approached, it meant breaking the ice but somehow my body had adjusted to the cold. The small wood stove kept us warm enough in the hide-out. Once or twice we were beset by visitors to the forest but the old man knew the place well and was adept at hiding and using lesser known paths.*

*Before I discovered the secret hide-out in the forest, I had seen the strangely dressed old man at the village market. He would wander back and forth, from stall to stall, in a haphazard way, until he had collected enough groceries at knock-down prices. He seemed deranged but harmless. The locals laughed at him, calling him the town tramp. No one suspected he might be the legendary old man of the forest, feared by the population.*

*Whilst we were together, the old man said little but his presence was somehow soothing and reassuring. I never quite knew why. Perhaps it was because he enjoyed the simple things of life and had nothing to prove. He certainly allowed Jake to be himself. Maybe I was learning something similar. I no longer wanted to impress but just to create like Jake. This began to give me great pleasure on its own; to find out what was within me and just let it find expression; that was enough. The pressure of having to or wanting to impress and perform was gone.*

*The weeks passed, turning soon into months. In that precious time, I got to know my brother in a way I had never known him before. His skilful hands and amazing dexterity made his carvings something to behold. I was in the presence of someone of extraordinary talent. Why did I never realise this before? I was now mesmerised by his artistry that had no doubt been nurtured under the tutelage of the old man. I grew to respect Jake and hold him in awe. I now realised that talent could remain hidden, if life circumstances dictate but, if those circumstances change, something remarkable could emerge. In Jake's case it had.*

*Although I frequently heard the sound of search helicopters up above, my fear of staying and being trapped in another existence was gradually overcome by fascination. Somehow it no longer mattered if I stayed or went. The old man had set about sculpting all the birds of the forest and Jake's work was integral to the project. There were robins, blackbirds, starlings, blue tits and countless other species. As the task neared its conclusion, Jake eagerly awaited the spring and with it the arrival of our final bird, the cuckoo, back from its long migration in Africa.*

*Of all these sculptures, the humble sparrow became my favourite. Jake fashioned a male and a female. They were beak to beak; the male bringing a worm to his spouse. The detail was phenomenal. Inspired by the old man, it seemed Jake had lavished more attention on these tiny and numerous little creatures than any other. And there were many other amazing sculptures: badgers, foxes, weasels, stoats, rats, squirrels and rabbits. Some of the sculptures were like a frieze, capturing an animal in the act of preying on its quarry.*

*This was a world in which I was led by my brother and I was* happy to learn. Other memories began to fade. Soon we were left to our own devices to explore the forest. As Jake drew the animals with skill and I mimicked him but with less success, we noticed the animals were no longer afraid of us. It was as if they became our friends as we became part of the forest. As we sketched them, their fear turned to curiosity and, before long, they were scampering about us, as if we did not exist. However, we soon realised that it was not because they did not notice us but rather we were accepted into their world.

One day, we were privileged to observe a vixen fox with her cubs. We had seen her and her cubs before. At first they had stayed close by her but now she took little notice when the cubs played around us. Jake had already chosen the wood for this sculpture. It seemed these animals knew our intention and were posing for photographs.

We worked together right up until late afternoon, when the light began to fade. I felt a oneness with Jake I had never known before. We returned from our labours full of excitement and anticipation. Jake had made copious drawings. He had carefully marked up the wood so he could begin the sculptures in the morning. We would strive together to make this our greatest work; well anyway, I would follow Jake's lead. The vixen would be caught in a dignified but watchful pose, her cubs suckling beneath her. While Jake worked on the main sculpture, I would work on her tiny charges. They would be positioned beneath on completion.

As we make our way back along a well-known path, Jake's mood seems gloomy. Normally he is chatty and excited about the prospect of working on new sculptures.

I press him, "Jake, what's wrong?"

Jake is silent. I see his eyes are red with worry. He speeds up and pushes through the bracken.

"Wait!"

Jake rounds on me, "Something bad has happened."

"That's ridiculous. Nothing's wrong."

The forest is unusually quiet. Normally the animals scuffle and run about us showing no fear. Usually we hear mating calls, and the birdsong is almost continuous when we explore the forest.

"The animals know. They sense things and I've learned to read the signs. They're telling us something."

Jake hurries and I can hardly keep up.

We return to the cavern by a new and trusted trapdoor in the forest floor. When we arrive it is silent. Normally, the old man is there to greet us. We have grown used to smelling the aroma of home cooking from old pots boiling on a wood-fuelled pyre. Jake goes in search of the old man.

Suddenly, there is a scream from the other end of the cavern. It is Jake. I rush across the space into the make-shift hollow the old man has been digging out. He is lying face-down in the dirt, the pick and spade by his side. Every few seconds his back heaves to draw breath. I act fast and turn the old man over. Jake becomes distraught. The old man's gnarled features are contorted and his lips quiver. His eyelids flicker and then open but he is unable to speak.

Jake buries his face in his hands and sobs, "My life is over. It will never be the same. My happiness is gone forever."

I place a hand on Jake's shoulder. Then the old man gasps; he is trying to say something so we draw in close.

*He splutters and grasps Jake's shirt, "Jake, you're the craftsman now."*

*His grip loosens and he slides back to the floor, his eyes staring.*

*"No! Not now. You can't die."*

*Jake is inconsolable for some minutes. Gradually, his screams turn to whimpers and eventually into a dull moan.*

*The next morning, we stand over a shallow mound of earth under the tree canopy. Jake kneels down and lays one of the old man's finest sculptures gently at the head of the grave. It is a tiny sparrow and the detail indicates how lovingly he has created this beautiful form.*

*Jake comments, "The old man always talked about the only thing he could remember from the Bible, back in his Sunday School days: the bit about the sparrows. Apparently it was something Jesus said; that not even one sparrow dies without God knowing about it and we are worth much more to God than many sparrows."*

*Jake stands up, "Even the sparrows mattered to old Larry." Jake brushes away a tear. It was the first time I had heard the old man's name.*

*Jake continues, "I learned that I really matter. God kind of communicated that to me through him."*

*I nod, "Come on Jake, let's go home."'*

---

**Exercise 10: 2**    Using the story **'Stranded'** or **'Aliens'**, rewrite the Story Climax so that it includes a Big Event.

...........................................................................................................................................

...........................................................................................................................................

...........................................................................................................................................

........................................

........................................

........................................

........................................

........................................

........................................

........................................

........................................

# 3. A Threat to Life

A **Threat to Life** can also bring a story to a close. The Hero Character's life is normally threatened by the actions of the Opponent Character, in either a direct or an indirect way.

Example:  Using *'The Operation'* story, show how a Threat to Life can bring a story to a Climax.

We rejoin this story as Robbie comes to terms with the fact that only the donation of his father's kidney can save his life.

*'The consultant turns back to towards me. He sees me staring at the door and comes over to the bed.*

    *"Don't worry, he'll come round when he sees it will save your life."*

*I study his features carefully and detect doubt in his eyes. I know if my father does not come back, I have little chance of survival.*

***The next day***

*While we sleep we have no cares. When I awake, it is to pain and discomfort. The room is a blur and I feel hot. Having a serious*

 ae

illness is like sinking into a miry swamp or quicksand. There is nothing you can do about it, unless someone pulls you out. The person supposed to do that is long gone. I can hardly lift my head off the pillow and my hands tremble, as if I have a fever. As I focus, I am aware the room is a hive of activity. The clock says 10.15am, so I must have slept for at least eighteen hours. Nurses check charts and whisper to each other about my symptoms. My eyes flicker under the glare of the strip-lights. There is someone at the foot of the bed. A tiny figure who stands motionless while people bustle past. It is Patsie. She slowly approaches the bedside table and places a card on it.

"It's from all of us, the whole class."
I try to smile but the pain from my abdomen is intense. Patsie looks away to hide her tears. She wipes her face and faces me.

"Even Eric feels sorry about his behaviour now. He's signed the card." Patsie reaches out her hand and places it reassuringly on my arm. I take her hand weakly and grip it.

I whisper, "It's bad, Patsie. I don't think I'll be coming back to school."

Patsie tries to sound upbeat, "It won't be soon but when you do, I'll sit next to you from now on. Every day I will, do you hear?"

I struggle with the words, "Thanks, but I mean, I won't be back... ever."
Patsie is dumbstruck, "But you..."

My mum enters the room with the consultant. She draws along-side Patsie and rests her arm affectionately on her shoulder.

"Isn't it nice Patsie came? And they're all missing you."
As usual my mother is alarmingly cheerful. This mood always hides how she really feels. She is always like this after my father

*has been hitting her. It's like a mask she wears when she cannot face up to things. I feel more angry than usual. My eyes lock onto Patsie's and I see fear in her gaze. I feel really alone and I know it is completely hopeless.*

*The consultant steps forward, "I'm afraid Robbie must rest now."*
*He checks my pulse and then listens for my heartbeat through his stethoscope. The nurse tucks in the bedclothes and puffs up the pillows. Her blonde hair glistens under the lights and her blue eyes blink with concern.*
*She smiles, "Now Robbie, it's time for your nap. They'll all be back later."*
*I slip back drowsily onto the pillow. I see the consultant whisper something into my mother's ear. As he pulls away he shakes his head. My mother gasps and puts her hand to her mouth. A gesture she always makes when she is really upset. She notices I am still conscious.*
*She chirps, "Dad'll be back, when he's had time to think."*
*Mother sounds doubtful and I can't stand it any longer.*
*I rasp, "I don't want him back!"*
*"Oh my dear, don't say that," my mother pleads.*
*I try to lift my head but I am too weak. The room becomes hazy and I feel sleepy again. In a moment I sink into peaceful rest.*

*A nudge and I awake. The consultant stands over me. He is tugging gently at my arm.*
*"Robbie, you have to wake up. I'm sorry, but this is urgent."*
*It is the middle of the night and lights have been dimmed. I can just hear the traffic noise outside. At least I am still alive. The*

consultant puts his hand on my forehead and turns to the nurse and whispers. I only catch phrases of their conversation.

"It's no use... there's only one thing for it... I agree."
My mouth is dry and my throat is so sore. I feel so weak. However, somehow my mind is clearer. Is this what it is like to die? Everything becomes crystal clear and your senses are sharpened.

Then there are more people around the bed. My mother stands weeping near the door in the shadows. I can see her chest heave with every breath. The consultant bends over me and whispers in my ear.

"Robbie, I want you to talk with your father."
He returns with the phone and pushes it towards my hand.

"We've tracked him down to a hotel on the other side of town."
I turn my head away.

The consultant takes a deep breath, "Robbie it's really serious; it's your only chance. Please!"

I stammer, "He hits my mum. He doesn't care about anybody."

"I know, but..."

I shove the phone away, "I don't want to talk to him."

The consultant goes to my mother and calms her.

My mother shrieks, "Please Robbie, please."
I feel the nurse stroke my hair and the warmth in her eyes melts my resolve. She slips the phone back into my hand.

"Come on Robbie, just listen to him, see what he says."
I pull the receiver up to my ear. I hear a crackle on the line and the sound of heavy breathing. The hum of night traffic almost drowns out the rhythmic inhalations of air.

*I hesitate and then venture, "Hello."*

*There is another silence, "Is that you, son?"*

*I say nothing. I can see my mum. She still stands by the door. As the headlights from below periodically light up the room, her face comes into sharp relief. The familiar bruises cover one side of her face. She strains to see through her swollen eye and the lipstick does little to hide the busted lip. No doubt she has told the doctor she fell on the stairs again. All I can feel is hate for this monster. I want nothing more to do with him.*

*"It's yer dad. I'm sorry about fings, yer know it's 'ard. I just... er, don't like 'ospitals. It's all cos' of me dad... yer grandad. They killed 'im. 'E just went in for a routine op and that was it, never came out again."*

*The phone hangs limp in my hand.*

*His voice gets louder, "Hey son, now you listen to me. I'm your father. You gotta understand. It's not that I don't want to 'elp, but..."*

*I whisper, "You're a coward and a bully."*

*"What! Don't you talk to me like that. Hey, do you 'ear? I'm yer father..."*

*I take a deep breath, "Not anymore!"*

*My mother breaks down, "No Robbie, no! You'll die."*
*The nurse comforts her and leads her from the room.*

*The consultant grabs the phone, "Mr. Edwards, you must donate a kidney if Robbie is to survive. You're his only hope."*

*I gather all my strength, "I don't want it. I never want to see him again. He hurt my mum."*
*The room starts to blur and swim and the words echo in my mind. I drift into unconsciousness.*

*I awake. The sun is shining through the window. The light*

*glistens off the nurse's blonde hair. She reaches over the bed to adjust the bed clothes. Her face lights up as she realises I have come round. She places a thermometer in my mouth and feels my forehead.*

*I whisper, "What's your name?"*

*She smiles warmly, "Staff Nurse Jeanie and you're my very special patient. You've been a brave and courageous boy."*

*The terrible pain is gone but I still feel discomfort in my abdomen. I reach down towards the bedclothes. Nurse Jeanie grasps my hand firmly.*

*"No Robbie, you had the operation two days ago. It will feel very uncomfortable."*

*I had survived. How had it happened?*

*Nurse Jeanie went to the door, "I'll tell your mother you've woken up."'*

# Exercise 10: 3

Using the story **'Stranded'** or **'Aliens'**, rewrite the Story Climax so that it includes a Big Event.

..............................................................................................................................

..............................................................................................................................

..............................................................................................................................

..............................................................................................................................

..............................................................................................................................

..............................................................................................................................

..............................................................................................................................

..............................................................................................................................

# Your Own Story - Draft Two

This is your chance to write your own story using one of the following scenarios as a starting point.

On the next page are two story scenarios. Choose either:

**Story 9 - 'Stranded'** or

**Story 10 - 'Aliens'**

• Use the learning points in this chapter to help you write.

• Write Story 9 in this book. Once you have learnt the principles, you can write Story 10 on separate sheets of paper.

## The Story Climax

Try and include ideas and techniques from this chapter.

### 1. Character Confrontation

A Character Confrontation brings the story to a head by causing the Hero Character and the Opponent Character to clash in a final Conflict. This could be a physical fight or battle, which might result in death. However, it can also be a verbal conflict, where the Hero Character's ideas or beliefs will usually prevail over those of the Opponent Character.

### 2. A Big Event

A Big Event can also bring a story to a close. This Event usually involves the Hero and Opponent Character but they are not always brought into direct confrontation. The Event could be a natural disaster or a personal tragedy.

### 3. A Threat to Life

A Threat to Life can also bring a story to a close. The Hero Character's life is normally threatened by the actions of the Opponent Character in either a direct or an indirect way.

Types of Story Climax can be combined. A Character Confrontation could involve a Big Event and a Threat to Life.

# Second Draft - Story 9
## 'Stranded'
## Opening Scenario in Past Tense:

'I dragged myself up onto the beach exhausted. The sea heaved as the storm raged on in the darkness. After choking and belching, I finally coughed up the sea-water from my lungs. For a moment I lay still; grateful to be alive. Eventually, I lifted my soaked and weary head and looked out across the lagoon. Just beyond it, the boat was breaking up on the rocks. It splintered, disintegrated and slipped beneath the waves. I turned and faced the shoreline. A long, sandy beach stretched out before me. As I peered into the gloom, I could make out the dim outline of palm trees and the silhouette of a mountain behind them. Where was I? I was stranded and lost. Would I ever escape?'

# Second Draft - Story 10
## 'Aliens'
## Opening Scenario in Present Tense:

'No one believes me. They all laugh when I say the aliens have landed. I finally persuade my friend, Lesley, to come with me to the clearing in the woods. By now, it is getting dark.

Lesley sneers, "What are they like, little green men with horns?" We trudge on silently up to the ridge above the trees. As we near the clearing we see a faint glow. Suddenly, we fall back terrified as bright lights come towards us. The woodland is lit up and the distant drone becomes a deafening noise. We crouch behind some bushes and shield our eyes. The blinding glare fades. There is silence.

I whisper to Lesley, "Now do you believe me?"'

Continue with either **Story 9** or **Story 10**, then use the Planning page to write down some more ideas for your story.

# Planning - 2nd Draft
# Story 9 - 'Stranded'

*It's time to plan a second draft.*

........................................................................

........................................................................

........................................................................

........................................................................

........................................................................

........................................................................

........................................................................

........................................................................

........................................................................

........................................................................

........................................................................

........................................................................

........................................................................

........................................................................

........................................................................

........................................................................

........................................................................

........................................................................

........................................................................

If you chose **Story 9 - 'Stranded'**, copy out the opening scenario on Story Page 1 - 2nd Draft, then continue your story on the pages that follow.

# Planning - 2nd Draft
# Story 10 - *'Aliens'*

*Let's plan a second draft.*

........................................................................................

........................................................................................

........................................................................................

........................................................................................

........................................................................................

........................................................................................

........................................................................................

........................................................................................

........................................................................................

........................................................................................

........................................................................................

........................................................................................

........................................................................................

........................................................................................

........................................................................................

........................................................................................

........................................................................................

........................................................................................

If you chose **Story 10 - *'Aliens'***, copy out the opening scenario on Story Page 1 - 2nd Draft, then continue your story on the pages that follow.

# Story Page 1 - 2nd Draft
## *'Stranded'* or *'Aliens'*

.............................................................................................................

.............................................................................................................

.............................................................................................................

.............................................................................................................

.............................................................................................................

.............................................................................................................

.............................................................................................................

.............................................................................................................

.............................................................................................................

.............................................................................................................

.............................................................................................................

.............................................................................................................

.............................................................................................................

.............................................................................................................

.............................................................................................................

.............................................................................................................

.............................................................................................................

.............................................................................................................

# Story Page 2 - 2nd Draft
## 'Stranded' or 'Aliens'

..................................................................................................

..................................................................................................

..................................................................................................

..................................................................................................

..................................................................................................

..................................................................................................

..................................................................................................

..................................................................................................

..................................................................................................

..................................................................................................

..................................................................................................

..................................................................................................

..................................................................................................

..................................................................................................

..................................................................................................

..................................................................................................

..................................................................................................

..................................................................................................

..................................................................................................

..................................................................................................

# Story Page 3 - 2nd Draft
## *'Stranded'* or *'Aliens'*

...................................................................................................................

...................................................................................................................

...................................................................................................................

...................................................................................................................

...................................................................................................................

...................................................................................................................

...................................................................................................................

...................................................................................................................

...................................................................................................................

...................................................................................................................

...................................................................................................................

...................................................................................................................

...................................................................................................................

...................................................................................................................

...................................................................................................................

...................................................................................................................

...................................................................................

...................................................................................

...................................................................................

...................................................................................

# Story Page 4 - 2nd Draft
## *'Stranded'* or *'Aliens'*

.........................................................................................................................................

.........................................................................................................................................

.........................................................................................................................................

.........................................................................................................................................

.........................................................................................................................................

.........................................................................................................................................

.........................................................................................................................................

.........................................................................................................................................

.........................................................................................................................................

.........................................................................................................................................

.........................................................................................................................................

.........................................................................................................................................

.........................................................................................................................................

.........................................................................................................................................

.........................................................................................................................................

.........................................................................................................................................

.........................................................................................................................................

.........................................................................................................................................

.........................................................................................................................................

.........................................................................................................................................

# Story Page 5 - 2nd Draft
## *'Stranded'* or *'Aliens'*

..........................................................................................................

..........................................................................................................

..........................................................................................................

..........................................................................................................

..........................................................................................................

..........................................................................................................

..........................................................................................................

..........................................................................................................

..........................................................................................................

..........................................................................................................

..........................................................................................................

..........................................................................................................

..........................................................................................................

..........................................................................................................

..........................................................................................................

..........................................................................................................

..........................................................................................................

..........................................................................................................

..........................................................................................................

..........................................................................................................

...................................................................................................................................

...................................................................................................................................

...................................................................................................................................

...................................................................................................................................

...................................................................................................................................

...................................................................................................................................

...................................................................................................................................

...................................................................................................................................

...................................................................................................................................

...................................................................................................................................

...................................................................................................................................

...................................................................................................................................

...................................................................................................................................

...................................................................................................................................

...................................................................................................................................

...................................................................................................................................

...................................................................................................................................

...................................................................................................................................

...................................................................................................................................

...................................................................................................................................

| **Scores Out of Ten** | Spelling & Grammar | → | ☐ | Creativity | → | ☐ |
|---|---|---|---|---|---|---|

# Marking the Stories

If you are working with a teacher or a tutor the stories can be given a Creativity and a Spelling and Grammar mark.

## Mark Scheme (marks 1 to 10)

| | | | |
|---|---|---|---|
| *Outstanding* | **10 marks** | *Acceptable* | **5 marks** |
| *Excellent* | **9 marks** | *Needs some work* | **4 marks** |
| *Very Good* | **8 marks** | *Needs a lot of work* | **3 marks** |
| *Good* | **7 marks** | *Requires more effort* | **2 marks** |
| *Satisfactory* | **6 marks** | *Rework it completely* | **1 mark** |

A mark below **5** means the story should be attempted again.

|  | Spelling & Grammar | Creativity |
|---|---|---|
| *Story 9 - '**Stranded**'*<br>*First Draft* | ☐ | ☐ |
| *Story 10 - '**Aliens**'*<br>*First Draft* | ☐ | ☐ |
| *Story 9 - '**Stranded**'*<br>*Second Draft* | ☐ | ☐ |
| *Story 10 - '**Aliens**'*<br>*Second Draft* | ☐ | ☐ |
| | Total Score ☐ | + Total Score ☐ |

**Average Score**
out of 10
(Divide total by 8)

☐

**Overall Percentage**

☐ %

**Total Score**

☐

# CERTIFICATE OF

This certifies

_____

has successfully completed

## 11+ Creative Writing

### WORKBOOK **5**

Overall percentage
score achieved

%

Comment _____

_____

Signed _____
(teacher/parent/guardian)

Date _____